The Wise Bear Stories
Helping you through life's journey

Criticism:
the truth everyone must learn

Scott Cranfield

Illustration Raphilena Bonito

The Wise Bear Stories
Criticism: the truth everyone must learn
Scott Cranfield

ISBN 9781912821068

A CIP catalogue record for this book
is available from the British Library.

Published 2019
Tricorn Books
Aspex Gallery, 42 The Vulcan Building
Gunwharf Quays
Portsmouth PO1 3BF

Printed & bound in the UK

Criticism:
the truth everyone must learn

How it Started:

Scott Cranfield the Author of Wise Bear has coached at the highest level for over 30 years, appearing on TV, radio, magazines, as well as hosting multiple seminars and being a key note speaker. His coaching covers subjects from life coaching and family relationships, to sport and business.

Since a young age I have been fascinated with and studied ways to help myself and others live the most inspired and fulfilled life possible. My journey has involved travelling the World attending countless programs and courses covering just about every area of life with the World's leading teachers.

As a father I wanted to share the best of what I had learnt with my children. I found a very effective way of doing this was through bedtime stories. I would create stories involving the challenges and anxieties my children had experienced that day and at the centre of each story is a character called Wise Bear. During the story the children would share with Wise Bear what was upsetting them or causing them to feel anxious. Wise Bear would use his vast experience and wisdom and share a whole new way of looking at these concerns to bring a calming balance to the children's mind, a balance they couldn't find on their own.

In each story the children learn useful tools and actions they can then apply for the rest of their lives.

My whole family are involved in bringing these stories to life, and it is our wish that these stories now help many other children and families, in the way they have helped ours.

Who is Wise Bear:

Wise Bear has been in the same family for generations. He has developed a unique wisdom that allows him to guide children, helping them dissolve their anxieties, as well as helping them make sense of the

different challenges and events they experience in their lives.
Every story covers a different subject, but within each story Wise Bear offers timeless lessons and vital life skills to help children navigate the journey of their life.

The lessons from Wise Bear will bring a calming balance to your children's mind, and give them a new and empowering perspective on any anxieties or challenges they face.

Even at 100 years old Wise Bear is still fascinated to learn and develop himself. He has had many brilliant teachers along the way, one special one he affectionately refers to as Dr D.

Wise Bear loves to read, exercise, make healthy smoothies and meditate. The only thing that gives away his age are some of his quirky sayings!

More than a story:
Each story ends with an affirmation and a short exercise to reinforce the lesson you have been reading about. This is a great opportunity to work with your children and help them apply the lessons directly to their own life.

Affirmations are a powerful way to develop strong and empowering beliefs for children, and the exercises give the children the opportunity to work through some of the challenges they face, so they can dissolve the anxieties and negative effects they hold in their mind.

Criticism: the truth everyone must learn

It was finally the weekend, and Mum drove to school to pick up Toby and Alex. She was looking forward to a nice couple of days of family time. The playground was full of other parents, looking out for their children. She spotted Toby and Alex.

"Hello!" she piped up, delighted to see them.

Alex ran towards her, a huge grin on her face. But Toby was hanging back a bit, looking sheepish. He was holding a note.

"What's that you've got there, Toby?" quizzed Mum.

Toby handed the note to Mum, shuffling uncomfortably.

It read:

> This note is to inform you that Toby has been in trouble today. He has been heard persistently calling his friend hurtful names. The other child was upset by his behaviour.

Mum frowned.

Toby didn't want to look Mum in the eye. They walked to the car in silence.

The first part of the journey home was awkward. Alex sensed that her brother was in trouble.

"So what is this all about?" asked Mum, perplexed. "This isn't like you at all."

Toby muttered under his breath.

"Come on, Toby, you can tell me. I need to know what's happened."

Toby closed his eyes slowly and breathed deeply. He knew that he had to tell Mum what had happened.

"Well, you know that toy car I really want for my birthday?"

Mum nodded, wondering where this was leading.

"Today Liam came to school with the exact same car! It's so cool – I've been wanting one for ages. I thought that if I made up a game where we could play with the car together, then I could have a go with it. But he just wasn't interested. I kept asking but he always said no!

"This made me really cross and I called him a few names. The teacher heard me and I got into trouble."

Toby slumped back in his seat, arms crossed defiantly.

Mum shook her head. She was clearly very upset with Toby.

The car parked outside their house and Alex scrambled out, rushing to the door to start her weekend.

Toby was a bit slower, dragging his feet and miserably sloping into the house.

"Do you have any homework?" asked Mum.

"Yes! I'm going to do it now, so that I have the rest of the weekend to myself!" replied Alex.

Mum smiled.

"And how about you, Toby?"

He looked up, still avoiding eye contact with Mum.

"Yes, I do have some homework, but I think I should go and speak with Wise Bear first."

"Good idea," said Mum, pleased that he was acknowledging that there was a problem.

They walked into the kitchen where Wise Bear was making himself a mug of green tea.

"Would anyone like a cuppa?" he asked.

"Not for me," said Mum.

"Nor me," replied Alex, more interested in a glass of squash.

"Yes, I'll have one please," said Toby. "And then can we sit in the lounge and have a chat?"

"Of course, old bean!" said Wise Bear, noticing a hint of sadness in his voice.

Toby was still grasping the note from his teacher.

"What's that note for, Toby?" asked Wise Bear.

Toby explained what had happened at school that day.

"Oh, I see. Good grief," said Wise Bear. He settled himself into the comfy armchair and thoughtfully stroked his chestnut whiskers. "OK, well here is some green tea for you. Come and sit down here and I can share something important with you."

Toby slumped on to the sofa. He had a feeling that he was about to hear an important but tough lesson from Wise Bear.

Wise Bear looked firmly at Toby and started his tale.

"There is an interesting law about humans that very few people understand and even when they do, they don't always want to believe it. But when you have lived for as long as I have you know it's true. I'm 100 years old, you know! That's quite old and although my paws are a bit wrinkly… Feel these!"

Wise Bear held out his furry paws to Toby, who rubbed them gently, managing a small smile. Wise Bear then remembered that he needed to share some important things with Toby and, putting his paws back in his lap, he continued.

"Anyway, back to the story. Toby, I want you to understand this lesson – it will help you a lot."

Toby managed to smile a little more. Wise Bear was quite a character!

"The law works like this. Whatever you see in the outside world is only a reflection of what you have on the inside."

Toby looked completely confused.

"Stay with me," said Wise Bear, "and all will become clear."

Toby nodded, confident that Wise Bear's words would eventually make sense and help him.

"Based on your experience today, this law would say that if you believe Liam was not sharing with you then you also know there are times when you don't share with others."

Wise Bear paused for a moment to let that sink in. He continued.

"One of the biggest problems in any relationship is when one person thinks they are right and the other person is wrong; or they think they are better than the other person in some way."

"Well, I do think that Liam was wrong for not sharing with me today," interjected Toby sternly.

"Hmmm. But before you really believe that, let's just finish the lesson," said Wise Bear. "Then see what you think."

Toby crossed his arms again and stuck out his lower lip. But he continued to listen.

"Toby, if you knew that what you criticised others for, you also did yourself, and if you also discovered the thing you criticised others for actually helped you in many ways, you would be less likely to judge others harshly and get upset with them. This knowledge would help you have much better friendships," said Wise Bear, the wisdom of his years shining through.

"Enough of the theory, let me ask you some questions so you can understand this law.

"Toby, use your memory and tell me times where someone has wanted to join in with you, or borrow something from you, and you haven't let them."

"Well, I'd always share. I like sharing my things," Toby said confidently. "If I had a new toy car, I'd share it with Liam. Of course I would!"

But Wise Bear, as an expert in human behaviour, wasn't going to let Toby get away with these excuses. All he had to do was stare at Toby, with a knowing look. His whiskers twitched.

Realising he'd been found out, Toby looked back through his memory. As he thought, his eyes looked up to the ceiling – he was remembering occasions which might be relevant here.

Wise Bear could see he was getting somewhere. He took a sip of his green tea.

"Well, there was this one time when I was playing a game with my action men and Alex wanted to join in and I wouldn't let her. I remember she cried because I wouldn't share the game."

"Ha! You see, old bean! Well done for remembering that occasion. But I am sure that there are others, so let's look again. Can you find another example of when you didn't share?"

Toby's eyes looked up again as he searched for examples

"Actually, just yesterday I was playing a computer game during afternoon break and it was Liam who wanted to join in with me, but I said no and blocked the screen so he couldn't see," said Toby, slightly embarrassed.

"Good example, Toby," said Wise Bear. "Keep going."

A moment later, Toby said, "Last week at lunchtime Mum had given me a few chocolate biscuits in my packed lunch and David's mum had forgotten to give him a snack. He asked if I could share my biscuits with him and I wouldn't let him."

Toby was no longer making excuses and the answers came flowing out.

"And in an art lesson last term, we had to choose our brushes for painting. Ruby came up to me and said she needed one of the brushes I had chosen. But I wouldn't let her borrow it."

In just a few minutes, Toby managed to remember seven examples of when he hadn't shared.

Wise Bear noticed Toby's facial expressions were changing and relaxing.

"Toby, how do you feel now?" quizzed Wise Bear.

"I definitely feel a little bit silly criticising Liam, now I know I do the same thing myself quite often."

"Excellent, Toby, that's great work! Now let's take this lesson a bit further so you can understand why everyone has these traits."

Toby gulped down his green tea, as he listened to Wise Bear's words.

"Remember today when Liam wouldn't share his new car with you?"

"Yes," replied Toby firmly.

"How did it benefit you that Liam didn't share?"

Inside Toby didn't really want to find a benefit, but he knew Wise Bear wasn't going to let him off the hook, so he delved into his memory.

"Well, at lunchtime because Liam wouldn't share I went across to the sports field and I actually played a game of football with some boys from Mr Pink's class who I normally wouldn't play with, and they turned out to be really cool kids and one of them has asked me on a play date, so that was a really good benefit."

"Marvellous! Well done," said Wise Bear, encouraged by Toby's responses.

"Now let's look at it from another angle so you develop a balanced mindset. When Liam wanted to join in with your computer game yesterday and you wouldn't let him, how did that benefit Liam?"

Toby looked puzzled. He thought this was a strange question.

"How would I know the benefit to Liam?" said Toby. "I don't think it did benefit him."

"Toby your mind is very clever. In any event like this, your mind will always know the answers if you ask the right questions, so let's try again," said Wise Bear.

"In your mind, go back to yesterday when Liam asked to join in with your computer game. From the moment you didn't share with Liam, how did that benefit him?"

After a moment Toby found the answer.

"I know!" he cried out, jumping off the sofa like an excited detective. "Liam spent that time to finish his homework, which meant that after school he could go and play in the park. But because I was playing my computer game in afternoon break I had to go home and complete my homework."

Toby was amazed that he had found these answers. Discovering this truth helped him feel much calmer.

In this lesson Toby learnt that he displayed the same traits that he sometimes criticised others for. He also discovered that these traits had benefits for him and others.

"It's really quite amazing how this works," said Toby to Wise Bear.

"Toby, when you're as old as me you will have seen thousands of situations where people have got upset at each other. If they had just taken the time to realise what they criticise others for they also do, it would help them appreciate each other much more. Toby, I am really pleased you have started to learn this lesson."

Toby was also pleased. He thanked Wise Bear and went off to finish his homework.

Later that evening, Toby saw Alex at the kitchen table playing a computer game on her tablet.

"Can I join in with you?" asked Toby.

"No, not really," said Alex, eyes fixed on the screen. "I want to do this on my own."

Toby was just about to start moaning and complaining to Mum when he remembered the lesson he had learnt from Wise Bear. He stopped for a moment and asked himself, "how is this benefiting me that Alex won't let me join in?" Almost instantly Toby remembered he had a Lego model to build, and he needed peace and quiet to do it. This would be the perfect opportunity.

So off he went to the playroom with a smile on his face and happily built his Lego model.

Wise Bear Affirmation: What you say to yourself can make a big difference to how you think.
That's why Wise Bear always recommends an affirmation to help you remember his stories.
Here is today's one...

"For every negative I can always find a positive."

Wise Bear recommends repeating these affirmations regularly. You can say them either out loud or inside your head.

Wise Bear exercise:

Use the questions below to discuss with your children and family how Wise Bear thinking can help you.

Write below 10 occasions when someone has done something to upset you, just like Liam had done to Toby. In the second column find out how their actions benefited you. In column three find memories where you have done the same or something similar to others as the action in column one. And then in column four find out how your actions benefited those you did it to.

Here is one example to start you off:

What upset you and who did it?	How did this benefit you?	Where have you done the same or similar and who to?	How did it benefit the person(s) you did it to?
My brother wore my jumper without asking	I chose an old jumper to wear and actually two people said I looked really cool	I took my sister's bike to my friend's house without asking	My sister ended up staying home and practising her handstands in the garden, now she is really good at them

What upset you and who did it?	How did this benefit you?	Where have you done the same or similar and who to?	How did it benefit the person(s) you did it to?

What upset you and who did it?	How did this benefit you?	Where have you done the same or similar and who to?	How did it benefit the person(s) you did it to?